COUNTRY LIVING
collection

Diary 2022

Personal details

Name

Address

Telephone (home)

Telephone (work)

Telephone (mobile)

Fax

E-mail

The date shown for the start of Ramadan is for the UK. It will differ by a day between countries, depending on the cycle of the moon.

*Provisional. At the time of printing, no changes to Daylight Savings Time had been confirmed by the government.

● **New Moon**   ◐ **First Quarter**   ○ **Full Moon**   ◑ **Last Quarter**

COUNTRY LIVING
collection

2022 year planner

	January					
M	31	3	10	17	24	
T	•	4	11	18	25	
W	•	5	12	19	26	
T	•	6	13	20	27	
F	•	7	14	21	28	
S	1	8	15	22	29	
S	2	9	16	23	30	

	February					
M	•	7	14	21	28	
T	1	8	15	22	•	
W	2	9	16	23	•	
T	3	10	17	24	•	
F	4	11	18	25	•	
S	5	12	19	26	•	
S	6	13	20	27	•	

	March					
M	•	7	14	21	28	
T	1	8	15	22	29	
W	2	9	16	23	30	
T	3	10	17	24	31	
F	4	11	18	25	•	
S	5	12	19	26	•	
S	6	13	20	27	•	

	April					
M	•	4	11	18	25	
T	•	5	12	19	26	
W	•	6	13	20	27	
T	•	7	14	21	28	
F	1	8	15	22	29	
S	2	9	16	23	30	
S	3	10	17	24	•	

	May					
M	30	2	9	16	23	
T	31	3	10	17	24	
W	•	4	11	18	25	
T	•	5	12	19	26	
F	•	6	13	20	27	
S	•	7	14	21	28	
S	1	8	15	22	29	

	June					
M	•	6	13	20	27	
T	•	7	14	21	28	
W	1	8	15	22	29	
T	2	9	16	23	30	
F	3	10	17	24	•	
S	4	11	18	25	•	
S	5	12	19	26	•	

	July					
M	•	4	11	18	25	
T	•	5	12	19	26	
W	•	6	13	20	27	
T	•	7	14	21	28	
F	1	8	15	22	29	
S	2	9	16	23	30	
S	3	10	17	24	31	

	August					
M	1	8	15	22	29	
T	2	9	16	23	30	
W	3	10	17	24	31	
T	4	11	18	25	•	
F	5	12	19	26	•	
S	6	13	20	27	•	
S	7	14	21	28	•	

	September					
M	•	5	12	19	26	
T	•	6	13	20	27	
W	•	7	14	21	28	
T	1	8	15	22	29	
F	2	9	16	23	30	
S	3	10	17	24	•	
S	4	11	18	25	•	

	October					
M	31	3	10	17	24	
T	•	4	11	18	25	
W	•	5	12	19	26	
T	•	6	13	20	27	
F	•	7	14	21	28	
S	1	8	15	22	29	
S	2	9	16	23	30	

	November					
M	•	7	14	21	28	
T	1	8	15	22	29	
W	2	9	16	23	30	
T	3	10	17	24	•	
F	4	11	18	25	•	
S	5	12	19	26	•	
S	6	13	20	27	•	

	December					
M	•	5	12	19	26	
T	•	6	13	20	27	
W	•	7	14	21	28	
T	1	8	15	22	29	
F	2	9	16	23	30	
S	3	10	17	24	31	
S	4	11	18	25	•	

2023 year planner

	January					
M	30	2	9	16	23	
T	31	3	10	17	24	
W	•	4	11	18	25	
T	•	5	12	19	26	
F	•	6	13	20	27	
S	•	7	14	21	28	
S	1	8	15	22	29	

	February					
M	•	6	13	20	27	
T	•	7	14	21	28	
W	1	8	15	22	•	
T	2	9	16	23	•	
F	3	10	17	24	•	
S	4	11	18	25	•	
S	5	12	19	26	•	

	March					
M	•	6	13	20	27	
T	•	7	14	21	28	
W	1	8	15	22	29	
T	2	9	16	23	30	
F	3	10	17	24	31	
S	4	11	18	25	•	
S	5	12	19	26	•	

	April					
M	•	3	10	17	24	
T	•	4	11	18	25	
W	•	5	12	19	26	
T	•	6	13	20	27	
F	•	7	14	21	28	
S	1	8	15	22	29	
S	2	9	16	23	30	

	May					
M	1	8	15	22	29	
T	2	9	16	23	30	
W	3	10	17	24	31	
T	4	11	18	25	•	
F	5	12	19	26	•	
S	6	13	20	27	•	
S	7	14	21	28	•	

	June					
M	•	5	12	19	26	
T	•	6	13	20	27	
W	•	7	14	21	28	
T	1	8	15	22	29	
F	2	9	16	23	30	
S	3	10	17	24	•	
S	4	11	18	25	•	

	July					
M	31	3	10	17	24	
T	•	4	11	18	25	
W	•	5	12	19	26	
T	•	6	13	20	27	
F	•	7	14	21	28	
S	1	8	15	22	29	
S	2	9	16	23	30	

	August					
M	•	7	14	21	28	
T	1	8	15	22	29	
W	2	9	16	23	30	
T	3	10	17	24	31	
F	4	11	18	25	•	
S	5	12	19	26	•	
S	6	13	20	27	•	

	September					
M	•	4	11	18	25	
T	•	5	12	19	26	
W	•	6	13	20	27	
T	•	7	14	21	28	
F	1	8	15	22	29	
S	2	9	16	23	30	
S	3	10	17	24	•	

	October					
M	30	2	9	16	23	
T	31	3	10	17	24	
W	•	4	11	18	25	
T	•	5	12	19	26	
F	•	6	13	20	27	
S	•	7	14	21	28	
S	1	8	15	22	29	

	November					
M	•	6	13	20	27	
T	•	7	14	21	28	
W	1	8	15	22	29	
T	2	9	16	23	30	
F	3	10	17	24	•	
S	4	11	18	25	•	
S	5	12	19	26	•	

	December					
M	•	4	11	18	25	
T	•	5	12	19	26	
W	•	6	13	20	27	
T	•	7	14	21	28	
F	1	8	15	22	29	
S	2	9	16	23	30	
S	3	10	17	24	31	

Welcome

Thank you for choosing this *Country Living* diary to record all your important events throughout the year. The ebb and flow of the seasons is such an important part of British life and our countryside, and every stunning portrait in this diary has been chosen to reflect that and inspire you. The images have all appeared in our monthly magazines and are the cream of a very superior crop! We hope you love our selection as much as we do. Enjoy!

Louise Pearce

Editor-in-chief
Country Living Magazine

PS For more details of the world of Country Living and our events throughout the year, visit *countryliving.com/uk*

December 2021/January

27
Monday

Holiday (UK, R. of Ireland, CAN, AUS, NZL)

28
Tuesday

Holiday (UK, R. of Ireland, AUS, NZL)

29
Wednesday

30
Thursday

31
Friday

New Year's Eve / Holiday (USA)

1
Saturday

New Year's Day

2
Sunday

COUNTRY LIVING
collection

3
Monday

Holiday (UK, R. of Ireland, CAN, AUS, NZL)

4
Tuesday

Holiday (SCT, NZL)

5
Wednesday

6
Thursday

7
Friday

8
Saturday

9
Sunday

January

10
Monday

11
Tuesday

12
Wednesday

13
Thursday

14
Friday

15
Saturday

16
Sunday

January

○

17
Monday
Martin Luther King, Jr. Day (Holiday USA)

18
Tuesday

19
Wednesday

20
Thursday

21
Friday

22
Saturday

23
Sunday

January

24
Monday

◑

25
Tuesday

Burns Night (SCT)

26
Wednesday

Australia Day (Holiday AUS)

27
Thursday

28
Friday

29
Saturday

30
Sunday

January/February

31
Monday

●

1
Tuesday

2
Wednesday

3
Thursday

4
Friday

5
Saturday

6
Sunday

Waitangi Day (NZL)

February

7

Monday

Holiday (NZL)

8

Tuesday

9

Wednesday

10

Thursday

11

Friday

12

Saturday

13

Sunday

February

14
Monday

St Valentine's Day

15
Tuesday

16
Wednesday

○

17
Thursday

18
Friday

19
Saturday

20
Sunday

February

21
Monday

Presidents' Day (Holiday USA)

22
Tuesday

23
Wednesday

24
Thursday

25
Friday

26
Saturday

27
Sunday

28
Monday

1
Tuesday

St David's Day / Shrove Tuesday

2

●

Wednesday

Ash Wednesday

3
Thursday

4
Friday

5
Saturday

6
Sunday

March

7
Monday

8
Tuesday

9
Wednesday

◐

10
Thursday

11
Friday

12
Saturday

Daylight Saving Time begins (USA, CAN)

13
Sunday

14
Monday   Commonwealth Day

15
Tuesday

16
Wednesday

17
Thursday   St Patrick's Day (Holiday N. Ireland, R. of Ireland)

○

18
Friday

19
Saturday

20
Sunday

March

21
Monday

22
Tuesday

23
Wednesday

24
Thursday

◐

25
Friday

26
Saturday

Mothering Sunday (UK, R. of Ireland) / Summer Time begins*

27
Sunday

28
Monday

29
Tuesday

30
Wednesday

31
Thursday

●

1
Friday

2
Saturday

3
Sunday

Daylight Saving Time ends (NZL, AUS – except NT, QLD, WA) / First Day of Ramadan

April

4
Monday

5
Tuesday

6
Wednesday

7
Thursday

8
Friday

◗

9
Saturday

10
Sunday

11
Monday

12
Tuesday

13
Wednesday

14
Thursday

15
Friday

Good Friday (Holiday UK, CAN, AUS, NZL)

○

16
Saturday

First Day of Passover (Pesach)

17
Sunday

Easter Sunday

April

18

Monday

Easter Monday (Holiday UK except SCT, R. of Ireland, CAN, AUS, NZL)

19

Tuesday

20

Wednesday

21

Thursday

22

Friday

Earth Day

23

Saturday

St George's Day

24

Sunday

April / May

25
Monday

Anzac Day (Holiday AUS, NZL)

26
Tuesday

27
Wednesday

28
Thursday

29
Friday

●

30
Saturday

1
Sunday

COUNTRY LIVING
collection

Cornflower
Centaurea cyanus
Wicken 18.07.19

Feverfew
Tanacetum
parthenium
Reach 06.18

Hydrang
macrop
Dorset 10.

orn poppy
apaver rhoeas
ubney Fen 22.07.19

Marigold
Calendula
Reach garden
06.18

Lark
Delphin
Wicken 1

Wild carrot
Daucus carota
Burwell Fen 07.19

Sweet pea
Lathyrus
odoratus
Reach garden
15.07.19

May

2
Monday

Holiday (UK, R. of Ireland)

3
Tuesday

4
Wednesday

5
Thursday

6
Friday

7
Saturday

8
Sunday

Mother's Day (USA, CAN, AUS, NZL)

◑

9
Monday

10
Tuesday

11
Wednesday

12
Thursday

13
Friday

14
Saturday

15
Sunday

May

○

16
Monday

17
Tuesday

18
Wednesday

19
Thursday

20
Friday

21
Saturday

◐

22
Sunday

23
Monday

Victoria Day (Holiday CAN)

24
Tuesday

25
Wednesday

26
Thursday

27
Friday

28
Saturday

29
Sunday

May/June

●

30
Monday

Memorial Day (Holiday USA)

31
Tuesday

1
Wednesday

2
Thursday

Holiday (UK)

3
Friday

The Queen's Platinum Jubilee (Holiday UK)

4
Saturday

5
Sunday

COUNTRY LIVING
collection

June

6
Monday   Holiday (R. of Ireland) / Queen's Birthday (Holiday NZL)

7
Tuesday

8
Wednesday

9
Thursday

10
Friday

11
Saturday

12
Sunday

June

13
Monday

○

14
Tuesday

15
Wednesday

16
Thursday

17
Friday

18
Saturday

19
Sunday

Father's Day (UK, R of Ireland, USA, CAN)

20
Monday

21
Tuesday

22
Wednesday

23
Thursday

24
Friday

25
Saturday

26
Sunday

June/July

27
Monday

28
Tuesday

29
Wednesday

30
Thursday

1
Friday

Canada Day (Holiday CAN)

2
Saturday

3
Sunday

4
Monday

Independence Day (Holiday USA)

5
Tuesday

6
Wednesday

7
Thursday

8
Friday

9
Saturday

10
Sunday

July

11
Monday

12
Tuesday

Battle of the Boyne (Holiday N. Ireland)

○

13
Wednesday

14
Thursday

15
Friday

16
Saturday

17
Sunday

18
Monday

19
Tuesday

20
Wednesday

21
Thursday

22
Friday

23
Saturday

24
Sunday

July

25
Monday

26
Tuesday

27
Wednesday

●

28
Thursday

29
Friday

30
Saturday

31
Sunday

1
Monday

Holiday (SCT, R. of Ireland)

2
Tuesday

3
Wednesday

4
Thursday

◑

5
Friday

6
Saturday

7
Sunday

August

8
Monday

9
Tuesday

10
Wednesday

11
Thursday

○

12
Friday

13
Saturday

14
Sunday

15
Monday

16
Tuesday

17
Wednesday

18
Thursday

19
Friday

20
Saturday

21
Sunday

August

22
Monday

23
Tuesday

24
Wednesday

25
Thursday

26
Friday

●

27
Saturday

28
Sunday

29
Monday

30
Tuesday

31
Wednesday

1
Thursday

2
Friday

◑

3
Saturday

4
Sunday

Father's Day (AUS, NZL)

September

5
Monday

Labor Day (Holiday USA) / Labour Day (Holiday CAN)

6
Tuesday

7
Wednesday

8
Thursday

9
Friday

○

10
Saturday

11
Sunday

September

12
Monday

13
Tuesday

14
Wednesday

15
Thursday

16
Friday

17
Saturday

18
Sunday

September

19
Monday

20
Tuesday

21
UN International Day of Peace
Wednesday

22
Thursday

23
Friday

24
Saturday

●

25
Daylight Saving Time begins (NZL)
Sunday

26

Monday

27

Tuesday

28

Wednesday

29

Thursday

30

Friday

1

Saturday

2

Sunday

Daylight Saving Time begins (AUS – except NT, QLD, WA)

October

◑

3
Monday

4
Tuesday

World Animal Day

5
Wednesday

6
Thursday

7
Friday

8
Saturday

○

9
Sunday

October

10
Monday   *Columbus Day (Holiday USA) / Thanksgiving Day (Holiday CAN)*

11
Tuesday

12
Wednesday

13
Thursday

14
Friday

15
Saturday

16
Sunday

October

◑

17
Monday

18
Tuesday

19
Wednesday

20
Thursday

21
Friday

22
Saturday

23
Sunday

24
Monday

Labour Day (Holiday NZL)

●

25
Tuesday

26
Wednesday

27
Thursday

28
Friday

29
Saturday

30
Sunday

Summer Time ends★

October/November

31
Monday

Hallowe'en / Holiday (R. of Ireland)

1
Tuesday

2
Wednesday

3
Thursday

4
Friday

5
Saturday

Bonfire Night

6
Sunday

Daylight Saving Time ends (USA, CAN)

COUNTRY LIVING
collection

November

7

Monday

8

Tuesday

○

9

Wednesday

10

Thursday

11

Friday

Veterans Day (Holiday USA) / Remembrance Day (Holiday CAN)

12

Saturday

13

Sunday

Remembrance Sunday (UK)

November

14
Monday

15
Tuesday

16
Wednesday

17
Thursday

18
Friday

19
Saturday

20
Sunday

November

21
Monday

22
Tuesday

●

23
Wednesday

24
Thursday   *Thanksgiving Day (Holiday USA)*

25
Friday

26
Saturday

27
Sunday

November/December

28
Monday

29
Tuesday

◐

St Andrew's Day (Holiday SCT)

30
Wednesday

1
Thursday

2
Friday

3
Saturday

4
Sunday

5
Monday

6
Tuesday

7
Wednesday

○

8
Thursday

9
Friday

10
Saturday

11
Sunday

December

12
Monday

13
Tuesday

14
Wednesday

15
Thursday

◑

16
Friday

17
Saturday

18
Sunday

19
Monday

20
Tuesday

21
Wednesday

22
Thursday

●

23
Friday

24
Saturday

Christmas Eve

25
Sunday

Christmas Day

December / January 2023

26
Monday

Boxing Day, St Stephen's Day (Holiday UK, R. of Ireland, CAN, AUS, NZL) / Holiday (USA)

27
Tuesday

Holiday (UK, R. of Ireland, CAN, AUS, NZL)

28
Wednesday

29
Thursday

◐

30
Friday

31
Saturday

New Year's Eve

1
Sunday

New Year's Day

Addresses

Name

Address

E-mail

Telephone   Mobile

Name

Address

E-mail

Telephone   Mobile

Name

Address

E-mail

Telephone   Mobile

Name

Address

E-mail

Telephone   Mobile

Name

Address

E-mail

Telephone   Mobile

Addresses

Name

Address

E-mail

Telephone   Mobile

Name

Address

E-mail

Telephone   Mobile

Name

Address

E-mail

Telephone   Mobile

Name

Address

E-mail

Telephone   Mobile

Name

Address

E-mail

Telephone   Mobile

Addresses

Name

Address

E-mail

Telephone   Mobile

Name

Address

E-mail

Telephone   Mobile

Name

Address

E-mail

Telephone   Mobile

Name

Address

E-mail

Telephone   Mobile

Name

Address

E-mail

Telephone   Mobile

Addresses

Name

Address

E-mail

Telephone   Mobile

Name

Address

E-mail

Telephone   Mobile

Name

Address

E-mail

Telephone   Mobile

Name

Address

E-mail

Telephone   Mobile

Name

Address

E-mail

Telephone   Mobile

Addresses

Name

Address

E-mail

Telephone   Mobile

Name

Address

E-mail

Telephone   Mobile

Name

Address

E-mail

Telephone   Mobile

Name

Address

E-mail

Telephone   Mobile

Name

Address

E-mail

Telephone   Mobile

Addresses

Name

Address

E-mail

Telephone   *Mobile*

Name

Address

E-mail

Telephone   *Mobile*

Name

Address

E-mail

Telephone   *Mobile*

Name

Address

E-mail

Telephone   *Mobile*

Name

Address

E-mail

Telephone   *Mobile*

Addresses

Name _____

Address _____

                                  E-mail _____

Telephone _____ Mobile _____

Name _____

Address _____

                                  E-mail _____

Telephone _____ Mobile _____

Name _____

Address _____

                                  E-mail _____

Telephone _____ Mobile _____

Name _____

Address _____

                                  E-mail _____

Telephone _____ Mobile _____

Name _____

Address _____

                                  E-mail _____

Telephone _____ Mobile _____

Addresses

Name _____

Address _____

                                  E-mail _____

Telephone _____ Mobile _____

Name _____

Address _____

                                  E-mail _____

Telephone _____ Mobile _____

Name _____

Address _____

                                  E-mail _____

Telephone _____ Mobile _____

Name _____

Address _____

                                  E-mail _____

Telephone _____ Mobile _____

Name _____

Address _____

                                  E-mail _____

Telephone _____ Mobile _____

Notes

Notes

Notes

Notes

Notes

Notes

Notes

Notes

Notes

Notes

Notes